Complete Guide to Learning Centers

SUPPLEMENT

Susan S. Petreshene

ILLUSTRATIONS BY ANNE DRUMMOND

THE SUPPLEMENT TO
THE COMPLETE GUIDE TO
LEARNING CENTERS

First published 1978
by Pendragon House, Inc.
2595 E. Bayshore Drive
Palo Alto, CA 94303, U.S.A.

FIRST PRINTING
Typesetting Lehmann Graphics
Printing: Banta West, Inc.
MANUFACTURED IN THE U.S.A.

ISBN No. 0-916988-13-9

Library of Congress
Catalog Card No. 77-71176

Acknowledgements

Many of the story-starters in this Supplement were originally drawn by Averil Anderson, a teacher of Petaluma, California.

Others were created by Anne Drummond, the illustrator of this book.

Still other story-starters sprang from the imagination of Florence Moon, also of Petaluma School District, and of Darlene Dinelli, a teacher in the Kentfield School District, both in California.

I am grateful for their permissions to include their materials in this Supplement.

On word-lists, I developed my Basic Spelling Vocabulary by cross-indexing three widely used high-frequency word-lists. These are the Madden-Carlson, the Rinsland and the Dolch lists, published respectively by World Book, the Macmillan Company and Garrard Press. Words which appeared on at least two of the three lists were compiled to form the Basic Spelling Vocabulary.

The Leslie W. Johnson list of "One Hundred Words Most Often Misspelled by Children In the Elementary Grades," is printed without change from The Journal of Educational Research *of October 1950. To W. Franklin Jones' list of "100 Spelling Demons," (included in* Concrete Investigations of the Materials of English Spelling, *published by the University of South Dakota in 1913), I made a few changes and added another 25 as yet unexorcised demons. Finally, I developed the "200 Important Spelling Words for Upper Grade Students," by utilizing the findings from two monumental studies,* Computational Analysis of Present-Day English, *by Henry Kucera and W. Nelson Francis, published by Brown University Press, and Ernest A. Horn's* A Basic Writing Vocabulary—10,000 Words Most Commonly Used in Writing, *from the University of Iowa. The first 236 words from the two lists were cross-indexed. The easier words from the compilation were then omitted.*

To all the above sources, I am grateful indeed.

Susan S. Petreshene

Table of Contents

Introduction

The teacher has permission to reproduce the following material (for use with children in his or her own classroom only). Explanation for the use of this material can be found in the following chapters of The Complete Guide To Learning Centers, *by Susan S. Petreshene (Pendragon House, Inc.).*

Chapter VIII, Individualized Spelling .... *pages 73-109*
Chapter X, Creative Writing Center .... *pages 161-166*
178-180

Story Starter Pages

There are forty different story starter pages in this supplement: twenty with dotted lines (primarily for use with primary grade students), and twenty without dotted lines (for use with upper grade students).

Pages 15 and 16 in this supplement enable the teacher to reproduce each of the illustrated story starter pages with or without dotted lines.

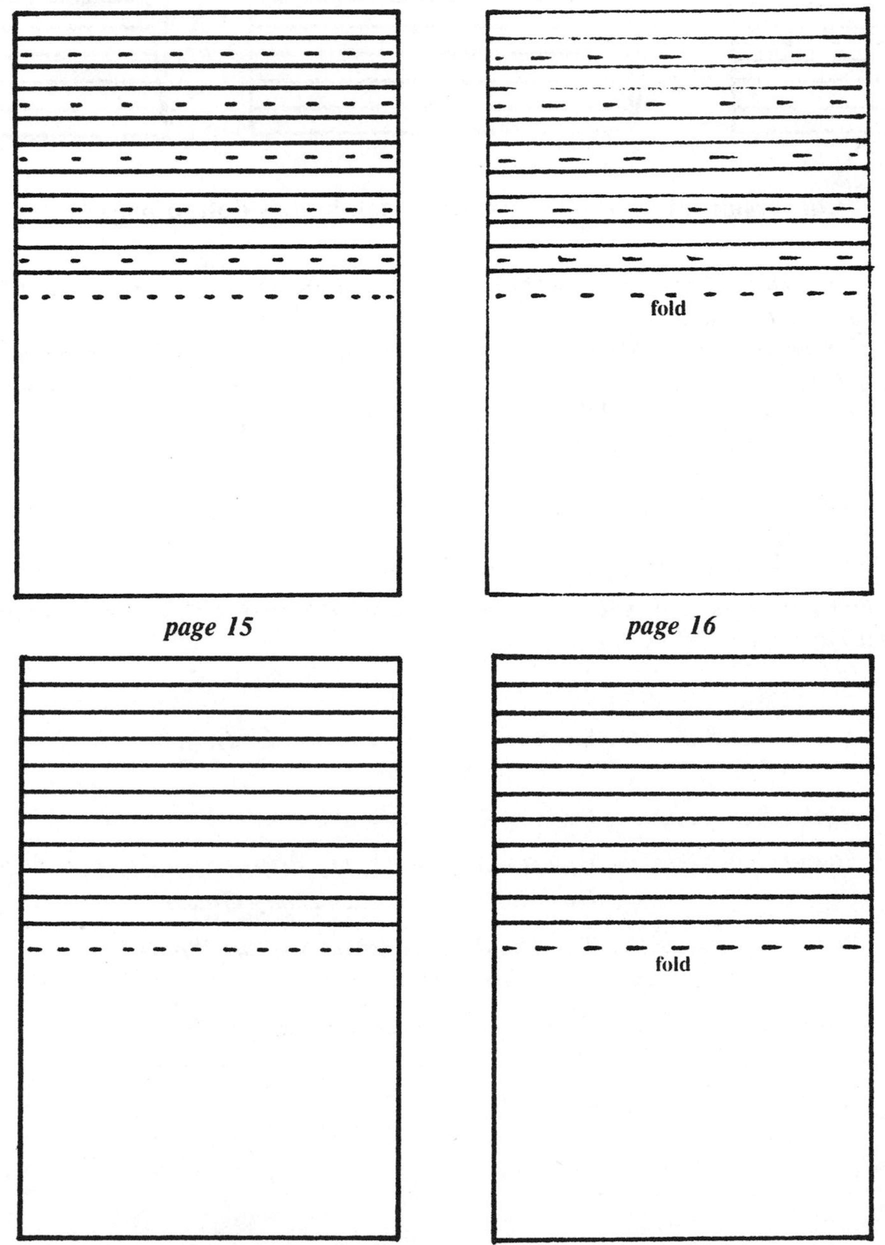

Conversion of dotted story starter page to non-dotted page

The following pictures illustrate the process of converting a story starter page with dotted lines into a page without dotted lines.

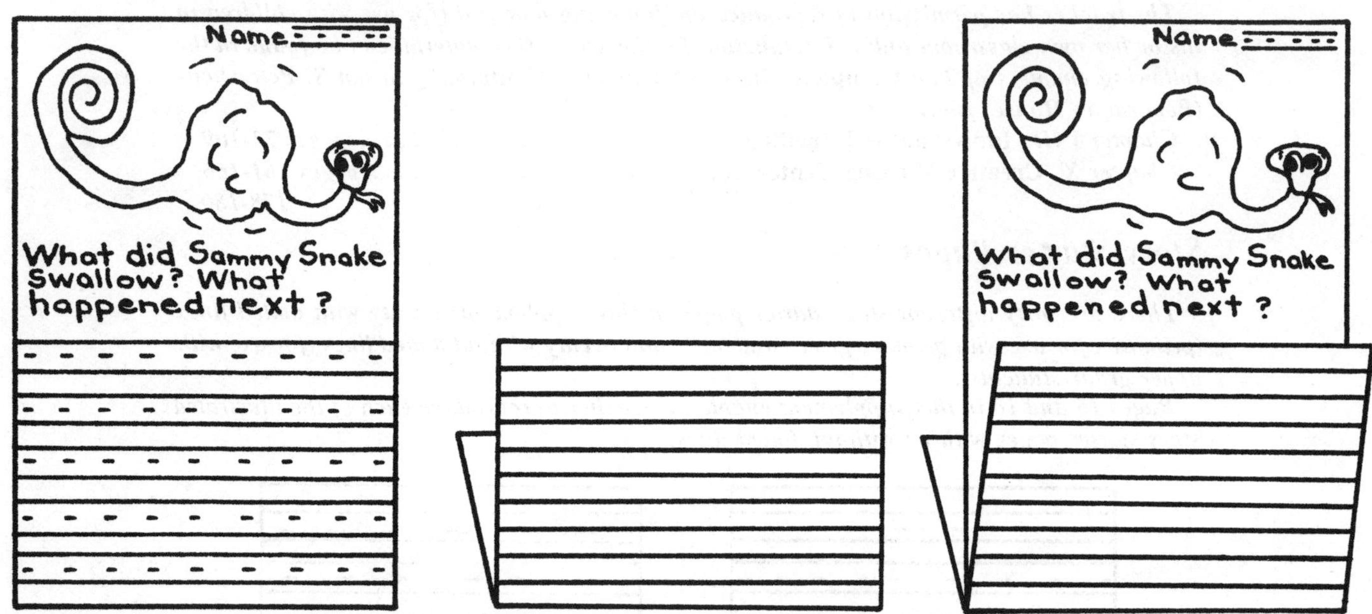

Conversion of dotted story starter page to non-dotted page

Pages 17 and 18 have been designed to be used as continuation pages for the two different types of story starter pages.

Please note pages 55-58. Although these do not actually involve creative writing, you will find they help you become acquainted with your students at the beginning of the school year. In addition, they can be used diagnostically to discover how well students follow written directions: "Put a line below . . ." "Circle the . . ." etc.

Spelling Lists

The coding system for the spelling lists in this supplement (pages 59-95) is found on the upper right hand corner of each page:

SV .... *Short vowel words*

S/L .... *Short vowels, long vowels, blends, and consonant digraphs*

BSV .... *Basic Spelling Vocabulary*

100/El .... *One Hundred Words Most Often Misspelled By Children in the Elementary Grades*

200/Up .... *Two Hundred Important Spelling Words for Upper Grade Students*

Phon. .... *Words to be used to work on specific phonetic elements*

Words for Primary Grade Individual Dictionaries

a
about
after
again
all
along
also
always
am
an
and
another
any
are
around
as
ask
asked
at
ate
away

baby
back
ball
be
because
bed
been
before
best
better
big
black
blue
book
both
boy
boys
bring
brother
brown
but
buy
by

call
called
came
can
car
carry
cat
children
Christmas
clean
close
cold
come
coming
could
country
cut

daddy
day
days
dear
did
didn't
do
does
dog
doll
done
don't
draw
down
drink

each
eat
eight
every

fall
far
fast
father
few
find
first
five
fly
for
found
four
friend
from
full
fun
funny

gave
get
getting
girl
girls
give
glad
go
goes
going
good
got
grade
great
green
grow

had
happy
has
have
he
heard
help
her
here
him
his
hold
home
hope
hot
house
how
hurt

I
if
I'm
in
into
is
it
its

jump
just

keep
kind
know

large
last
laugh
let
letter
light
like
little
live
long
look
looked
lot
lots
love

made
make
man
many
may
me
men
milk
more
morning
most
mother
much
must
my
myself

name
never
new
next
nice
night
no
not
now

of
off
old
on
once
one
only
open
or
other
our
out
over
own

people
pick
place
play
played
please
pretty
pull
put

ran
read
red
right
room
round
run

said
Santa Claus
saw
say
school
see
seven
shall
she
should
show
sing
sister
sit
six
sleep
small
snow
so
some
something
soon
start
started
step
summer
sure

No "Qq" words are included on this dictionary list.

take
teacher
tell
ten
than
thank
that
the
their
them
there
these
they
thing
things
think
this
those
thought
three
through
time
to
today
together
told
too
took
tows
tree
try
two

under
until
up
upon
us
use

very

walk
want
wanted
warm
was
wash
water
way
we
week
well
went
were
what
when
where
which
while
white
who
why
will
wish
with
work
would
write

year
years
yellow
yes
you
your

No "Xx" or "Zz" words are included on this dictionary list.

Words for Upper Grade Individual Dictionaries

about
after
again
against
all
almost
along
also
always
American
among
another
any
are
around
ask
asked
away

back
being
because
become
been
before
best
better
between
black
blue
book
both
boys
bring
brother
brown
business
buy
by

called
came
car
carry
case
children
Christmas
city
clean
close
cold
come
coming
could
course
country

days
dear
didn't
do
does
done
don't
door
down
draw
drink
during

each
early
eat
eight
end
enough
even
every
eyes

face
fact
far
father
few
find
first
fly
for
form
found
four
friend
from
full
fun
funny

gave
general
getting
girls
give
given
goes
going
good
government
grade
great
group
grow

hand
happy
have
head
heard
help
her
here
high
himself
hold
home
hope
house
how
however
hurt

important
its
it's

just

kind
knew
know

large
last
later
laugh
left
less
letter
life
light
like
little
live
long
looked

made
make
many
may
men
might
more
morning
most
mother
Mr.
Mrs.
much
must
myself

national
need
never
new
next
nice
night
nothing
now
number

of
off
often
old
once
one
only
open
or
order
other
our
out
over
own

part
people
per
pick
place
played
please
point
possible
present
president
pretty
program
public
pull
put

rather
read
right
room
round

said
same
saw
say
school
second
set
several
shall
should
show
since
sister
sleep
small
snow
social
some
something
soon
started
state
states
still
such
summer
sure
system

No "Qq" words are included on this dictionary list.

take
teacher
than
thank
their
them
then
there
these
they
things
think
this
those
though
thought
three
through
time
today
together

told
too
took
toward
town
tree
try
two

under
until
united
upon
us
use
used

very

walk
want
wanted
war
warm
was
wash
water
way
week
well
went
were
what
when
where
which
while
white
who
why
will
wish

within
without
work
world
would
write

year
yellow
yet
you
young
your

No "Xx" or "Zz" words are included on this dictionary list.

fold

Please look at the three parallel pictures in the Introduction to see how to convert a story-starter page, without dotted lines, into a page with dotted lines.

fold

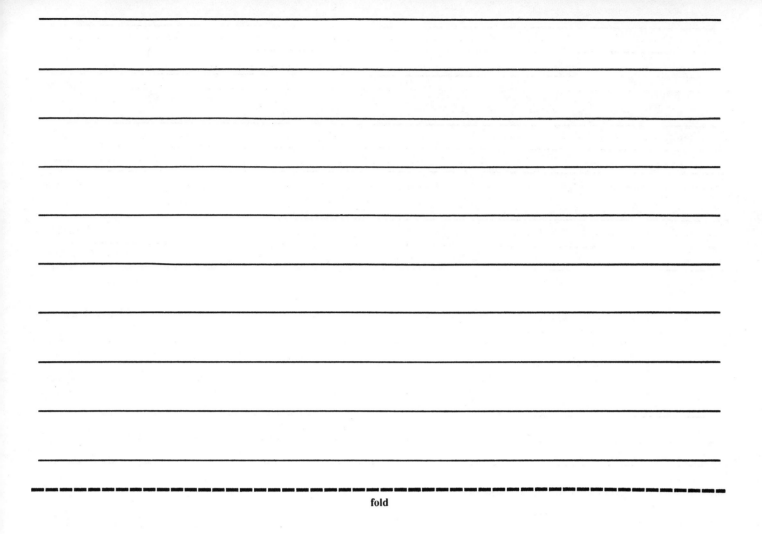

Please look at the three parallel pictures in the Introduction to see how to convert a story-starter page, with dotted lines, into a page without dotted lines.

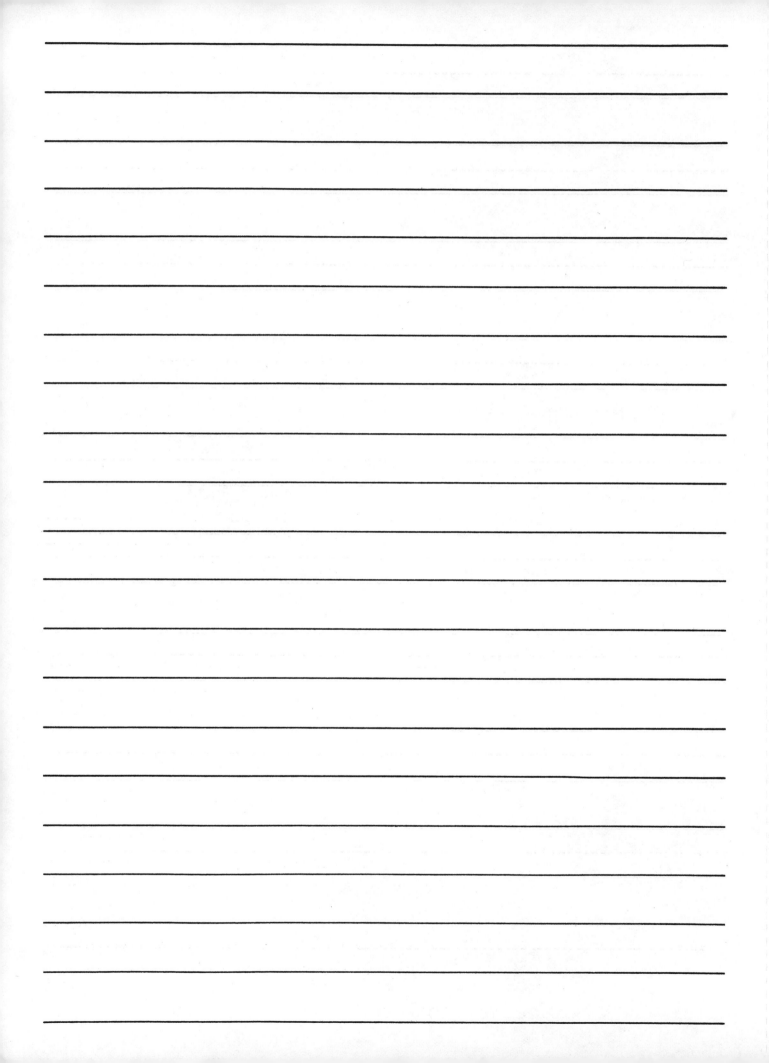

Name ____________________

Whose Eyes are These?

(1.) 

(2.) 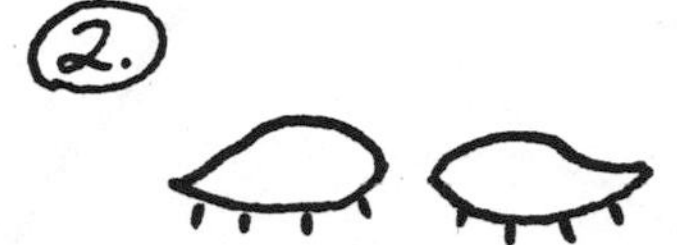

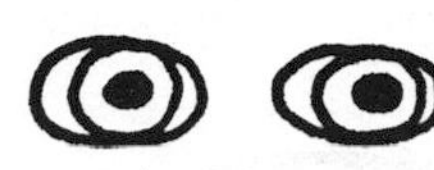

Draw the rest of the face.
Tell who each one is.

(1.) I am ____________________

I live in ____________________

(2.) I am ____________________

I live in ____________________

(3.) I am ____________________

I live in ____________________

Name ____________________

What did Sammy Snake swallow ?

What happened next ?

Name ____________________

Why is this elephant hiding?

Name ______________________

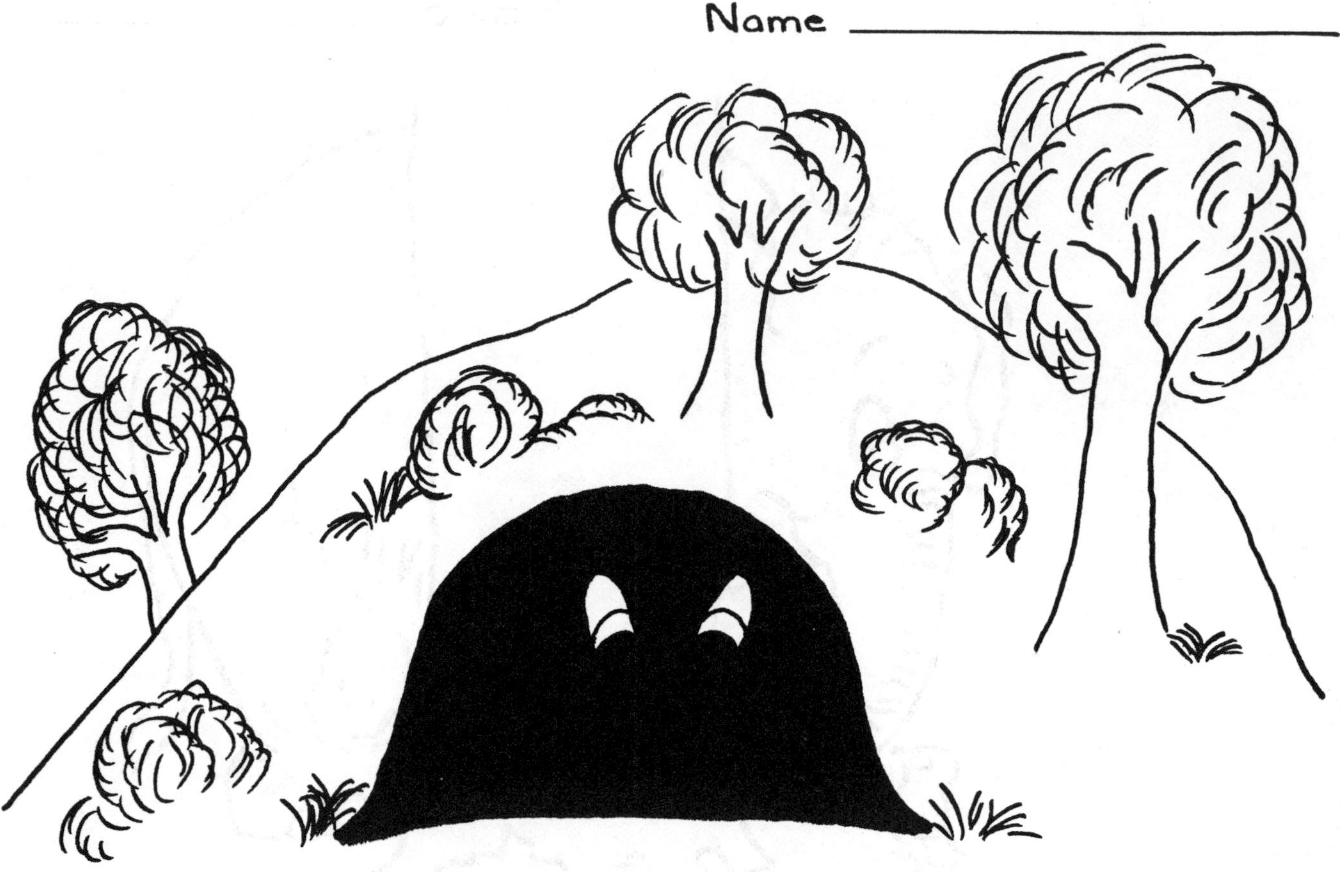

What is inside the cave ?

Name ______________________

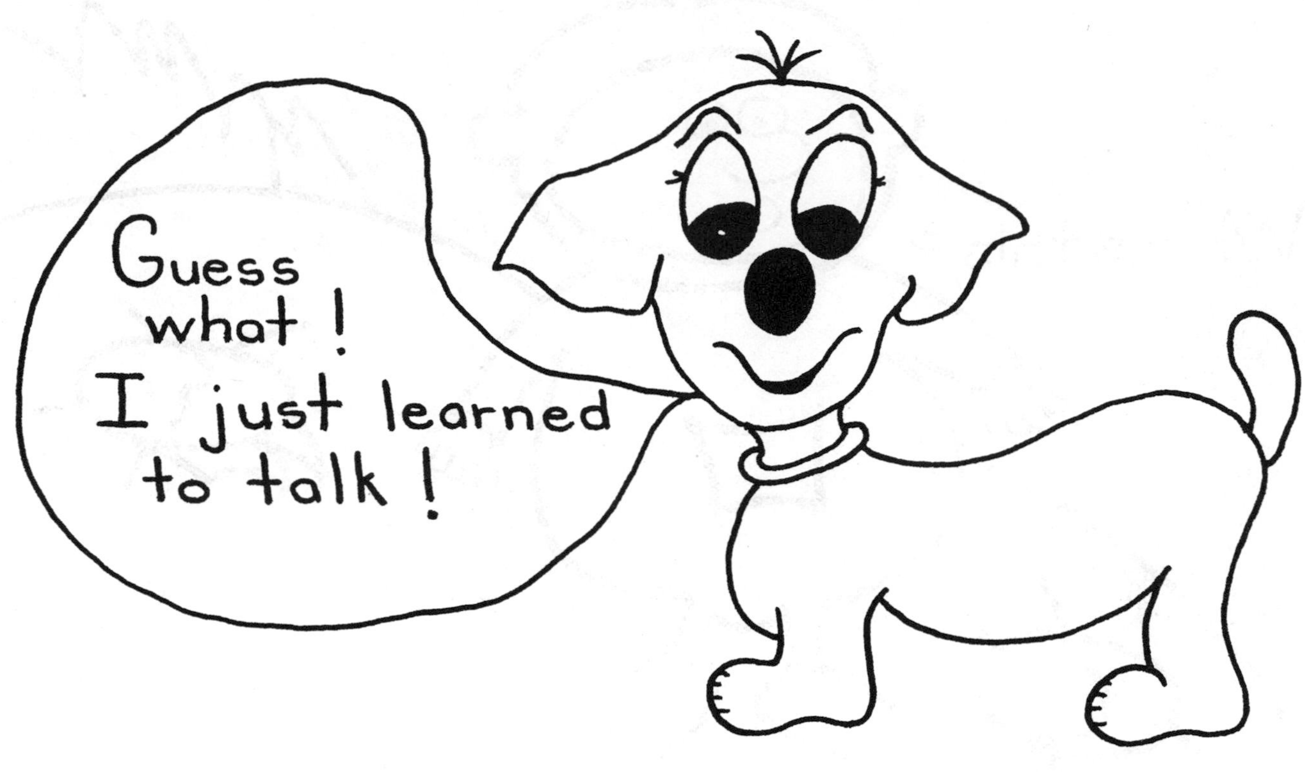
Guess what ! I just learned to talk !

Name ______________________

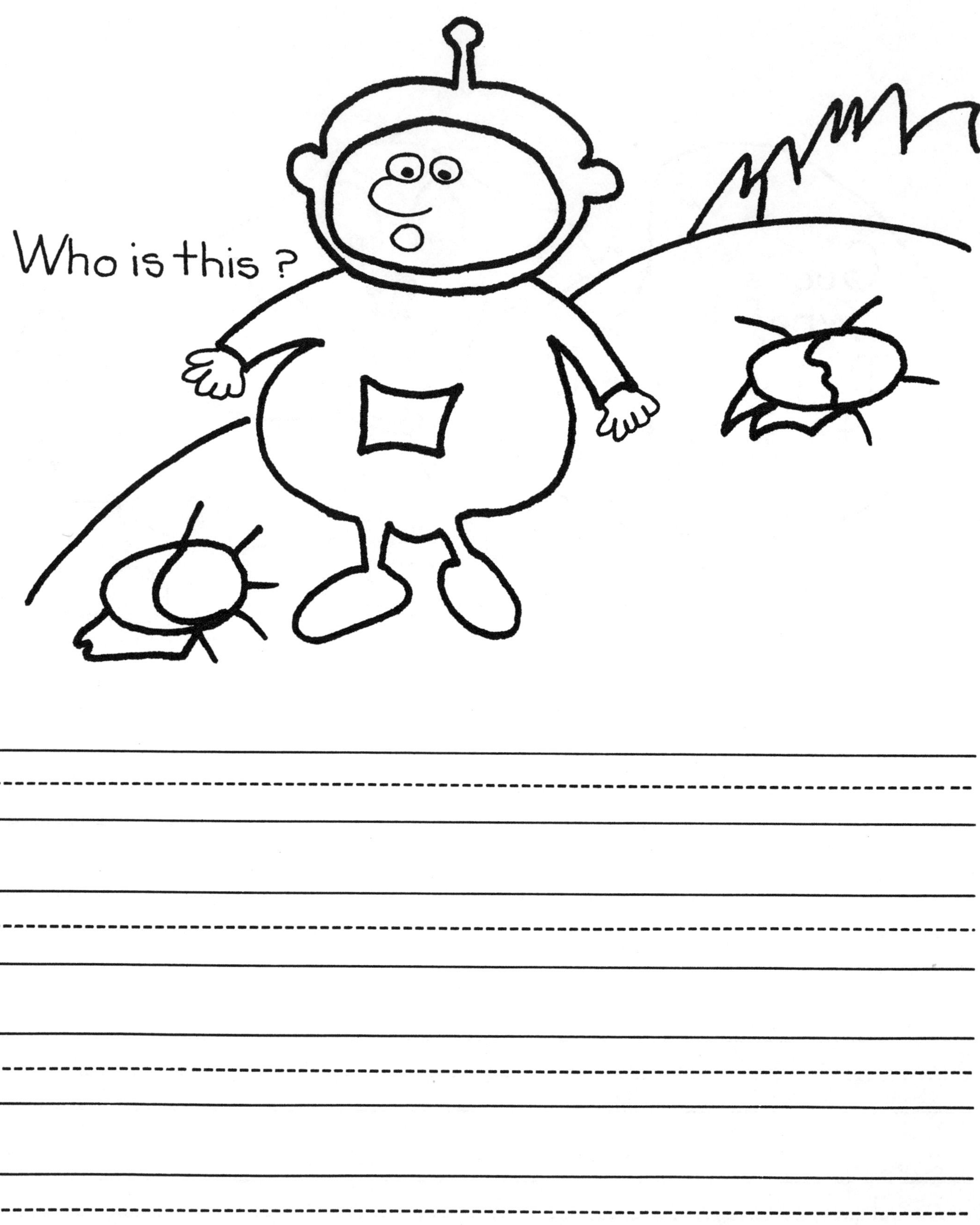

Name ____________________

What do you think has happened? What are they saying?

Name ____________________

Who lives here ?

Name ____________________

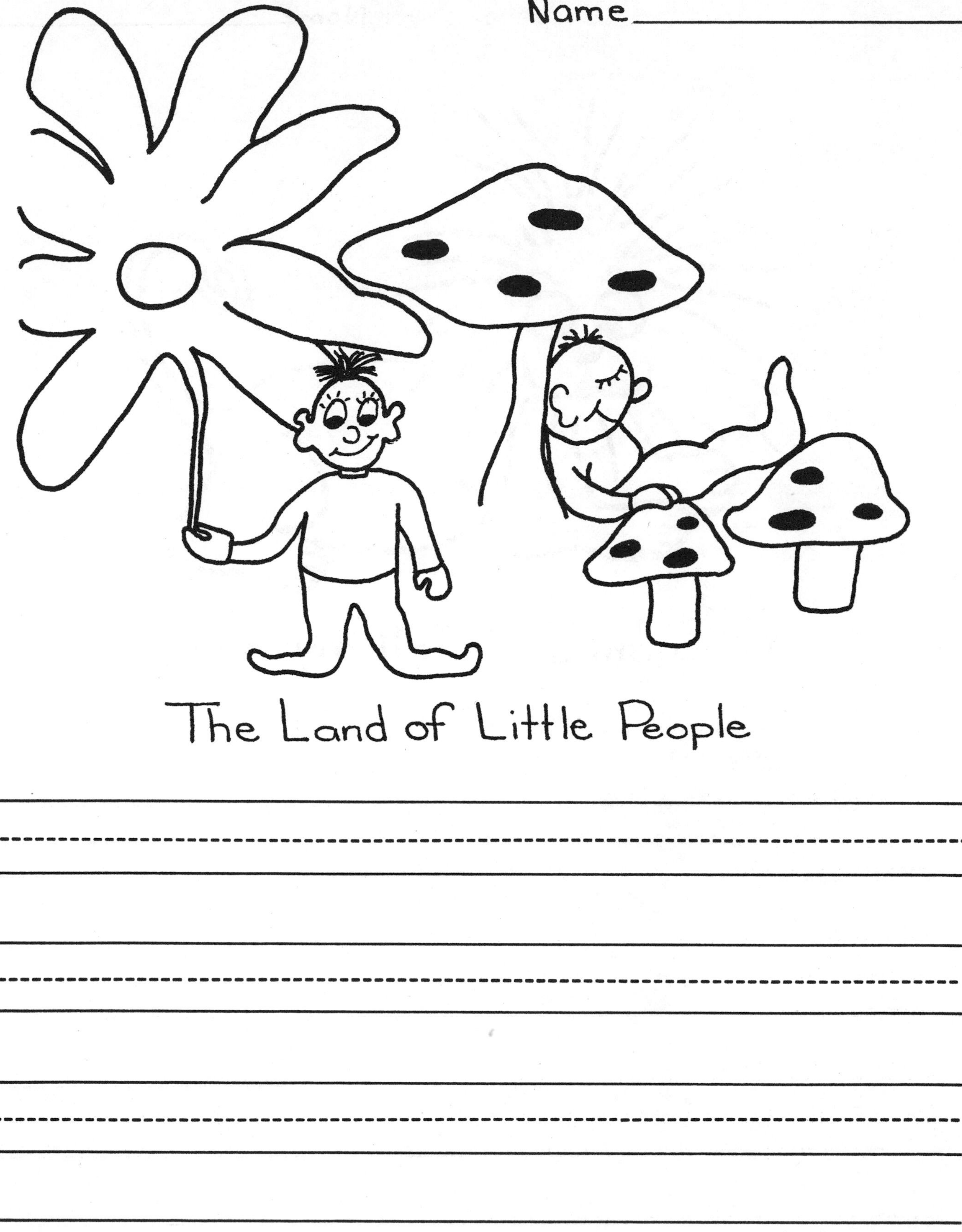

The Land of Little People

Name ____________________

Who am I ? Tell my story.

Name________________

Where are all the little creatures going? Why?

Name ______________________

I am
hiding. Who
am I ?
Why am I
hiding?

Name ______________________

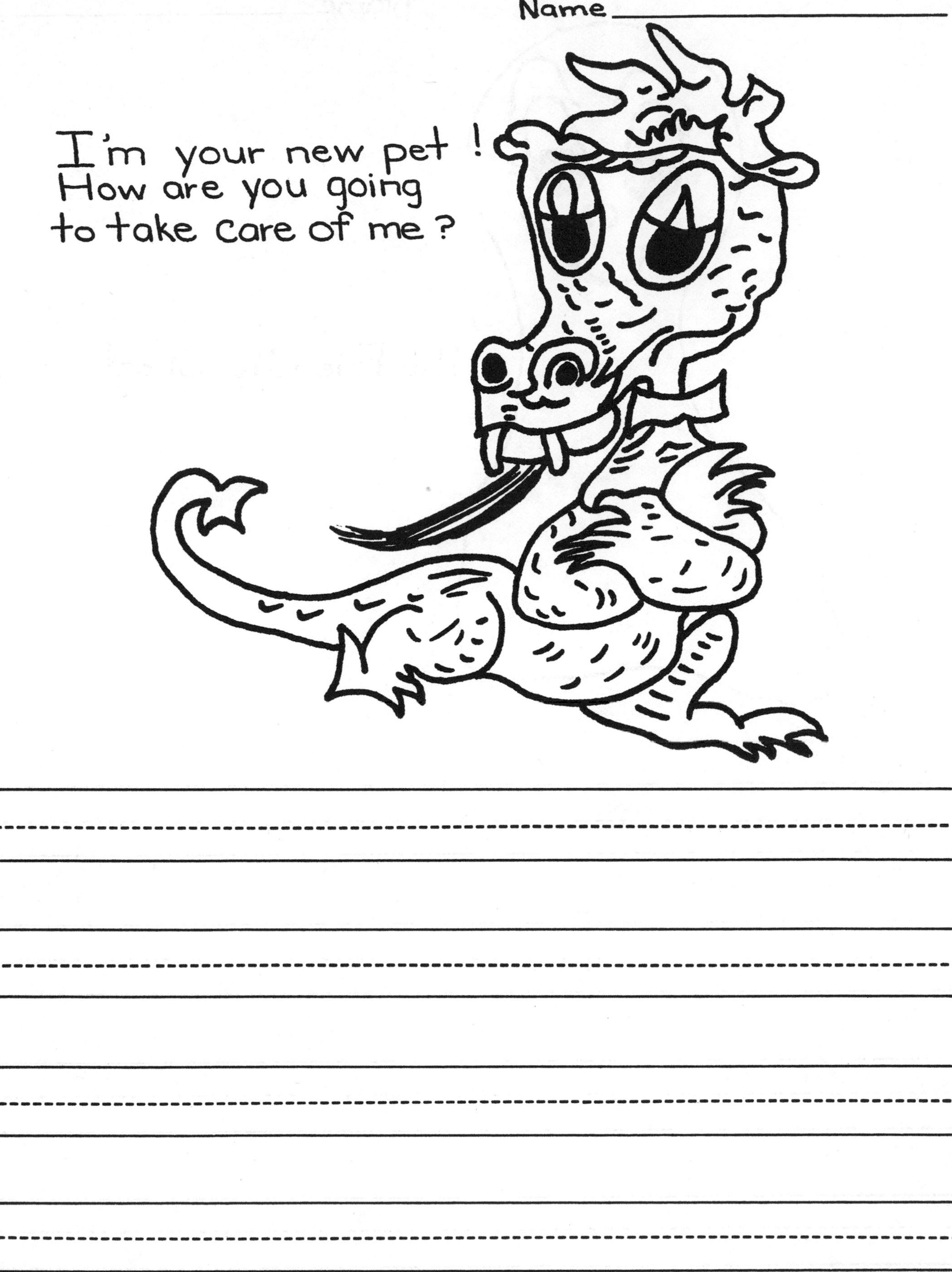
I'm your new pet ! How are you going to take care of me ?

Name________________

The Friendly Ghost

Name ____________________

Who or what is under the hat? What is it called? How did it get there? What is it doing there now?

Name ____________

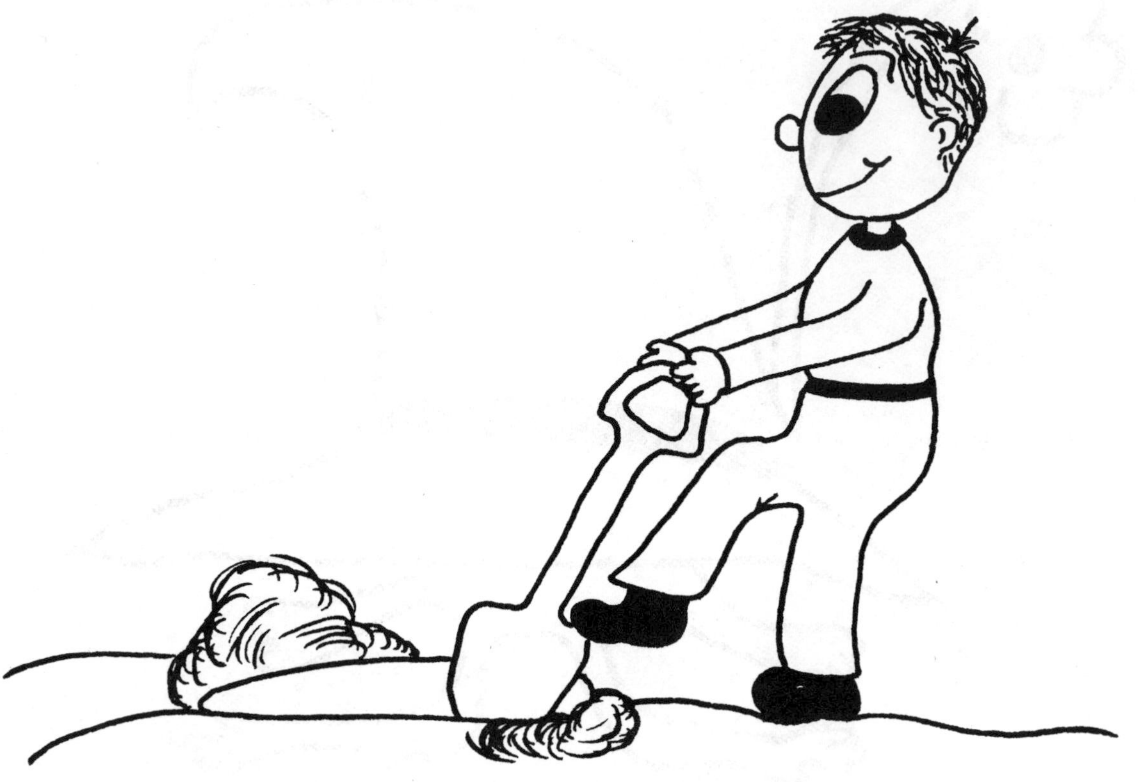

The Buried Treasure

Name ____________________

What would you do if you found a Martian in your backyard?

Name ______________________

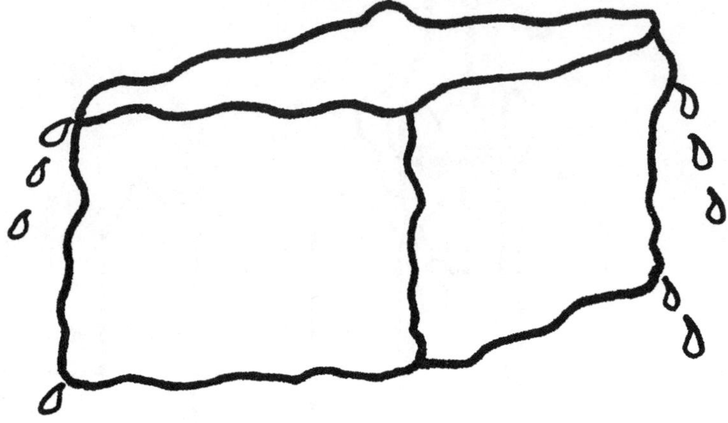

This is a block of ice.
You were frozen in there.
How did it happen?
What will you do about it?

Name ____________________

Write a story about the day you went to the zoo and discovered when you spoke to the animals they spoke back.

Name____________________

In the classroom I like

____

____________________ (List three things).

____

But the one I like best is ____________

__________________ because __________________

____

I don't like to ____________________________

because ________________________________

____

If I could change some things in the room, I wish we would

____

____

Name ____________________

Write a story about the day you won the Indy 500.

Name ____________________

Who is this ?

____

____

____

____

____

____

____

____

Name ____________________

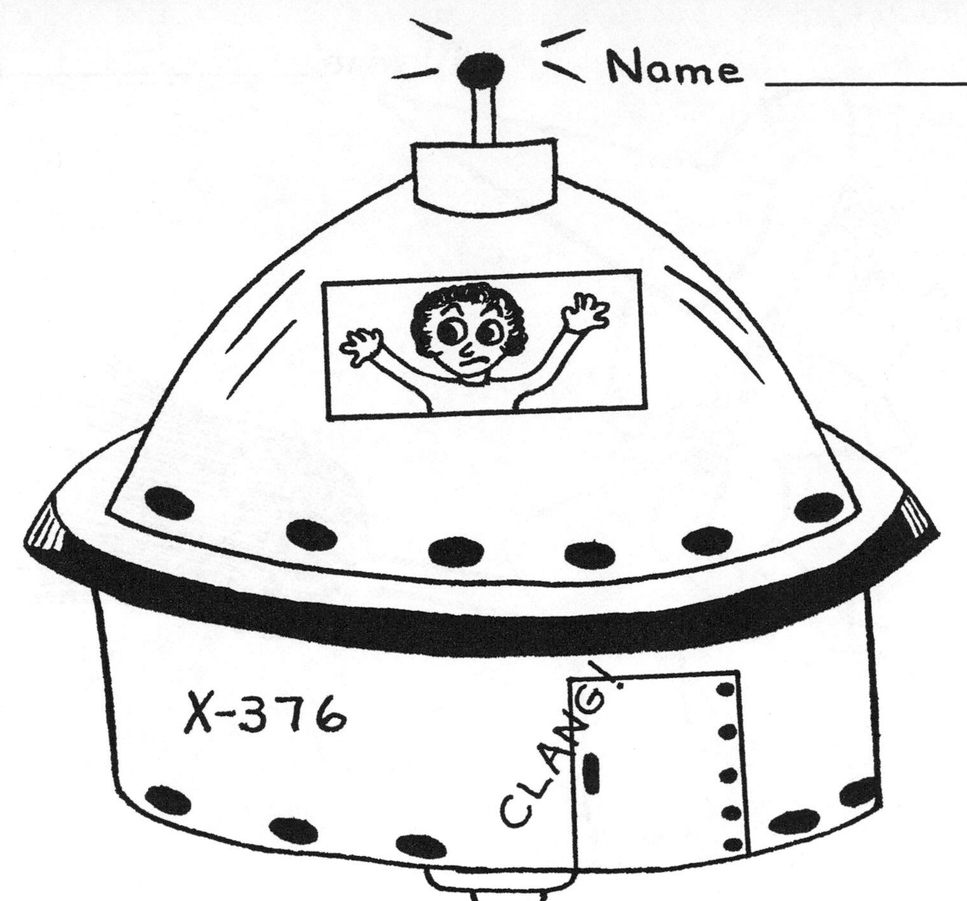

You have crept aboard a space ship to take a secret look. Suddenly Clang ... the door closes.

Name ____________________

You are trick or treating with some friends. Suddenly a witch appears in front of you. What happened?

Name ______________________

You'll never believe this, but last Saturday when I woke up, I discovered I'd turned into a . . .

____

____

____

____

____

____

____

____

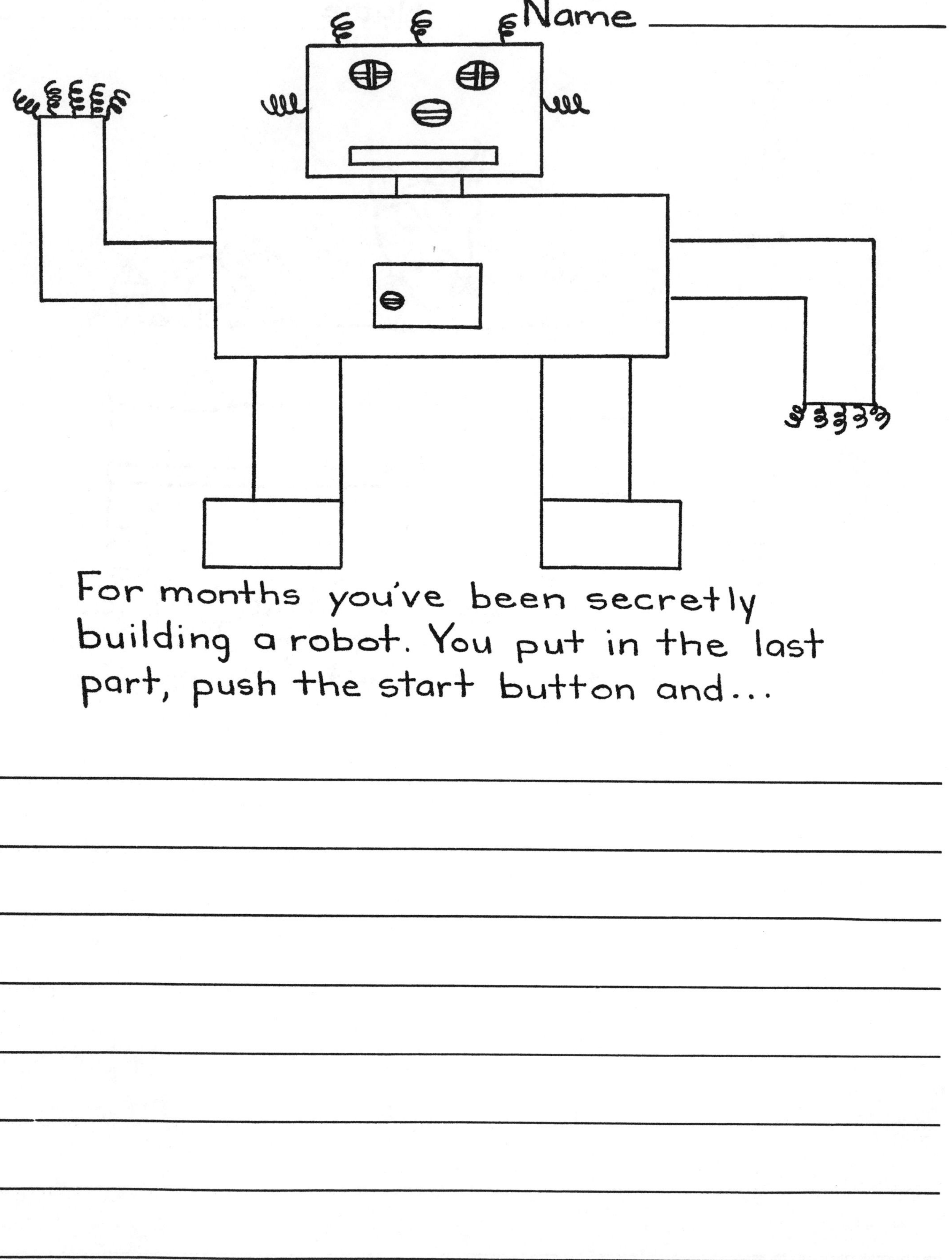
Name
For months you've been secretly building a robot. You put in the last part, push the start button and...

Name ____________________

Name ____________________

One morning you wake up and realize it's the year 2077. What do you see and do ?

____

____

____

____

____

____

____

____

Name ____________________

Mr.________the____________

____

____

____

____

____

____

____

____

Name________________________

Everyone said it wouldn't float. Despite them all, I climbed in my bathtub boat and...

____

____

____

____

____

____

____

____

Name ____________________

You received a chemistry set for your birthday. Everyone has gone to bed, but you decide to try an experiment ...

Name ______________________

Write a story about YOU as the most valuable player in the game that won the world series.

____

____

____

____

____

____

____

____

Name ____________________

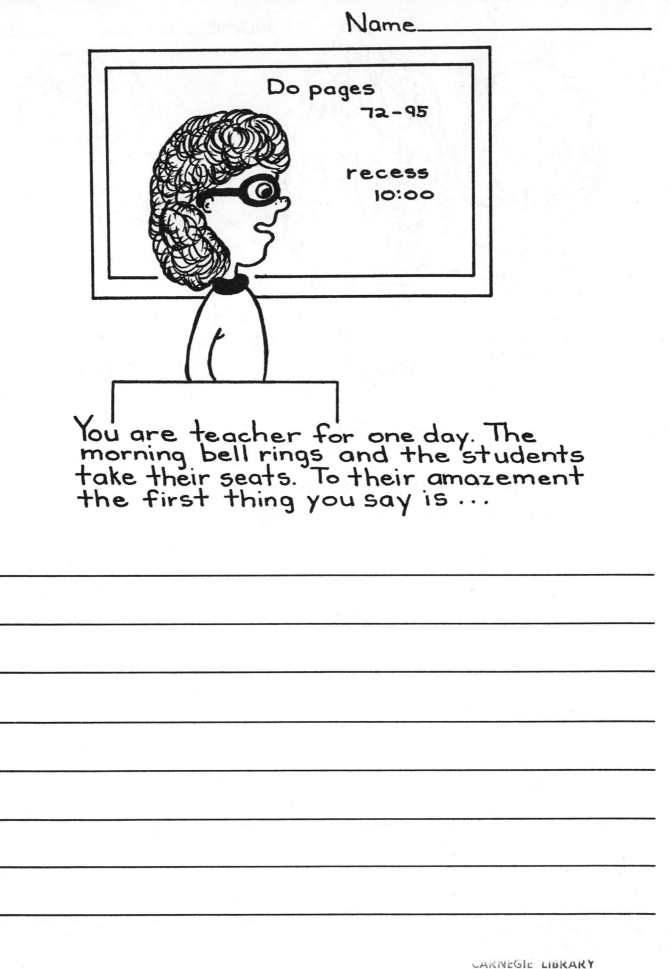

You are teacher for one day. The morning bell rings and the students take their seats. To their amazement the first thing you say is . . .

Name ______________________

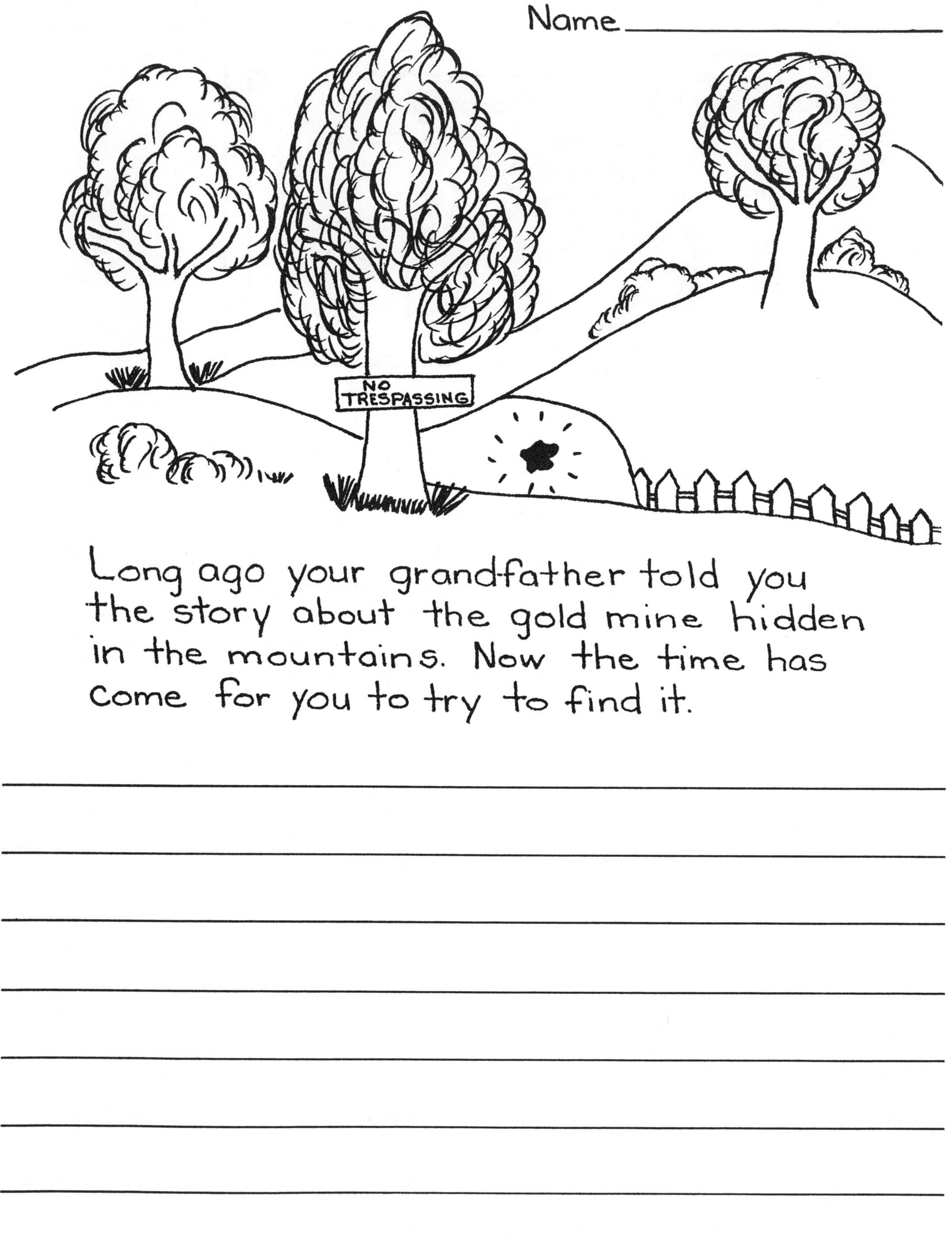

Long ago your grandfather told you the story about the gold mine hidden in the mountains. Now the time has come for you to try to find it.

Name ______________________

One day while you were playing alone in the attic you saw an old trunk covered with dust. When you opened it you saw some unusual yellow powder in the bottom. As you picked up some of the powder you felt strange and then you realized you were becoming invisible!

____

____

____

____

____

____

____

____

Name ____________________

I was walking through the forest when suddenly a small voice called out to me. I looked around. Where did it come from? What was it? Then I saw...

1. Write your whole name.

____

____

2. Write your address.

   (street) ______________________________

   (city, state) ______________________________

   ____

3. Write your phone number. ________________
4. How many people are in your family? __________
5. How many pets do you have? ____________
6. What is your favorite color? ____________
7. When is your birthday? ______________
8. What is your favorite food?

____

____

9. What is your favorite T.V. program?

____

____

10. What is your favorite thing to do?

____

____

____

____

____

What do you know about YOURSELF ?

① Do you like one friend or many ?

____

____

② Are you easy to get along with ? (Circle the answer).

Yes   Sometimes   No

③ Do you think there should be class rules for all to follow ?

Which do you think are most important?

____

____

____

④ Are you good at following rules ? (Circle the answer).

Very good   good   not so good

⑤ Do you like to help others when you can? ______________________________

⑥ Would you let someone help you ?

____

Thinking About School

① What do you like about school?

____

____

____

____

② What do you dislike about school?

____

____

____

____

③ Are you good in P.E. ? ________________

④ What's your favorite sport? (circle answer).

football   handball   relay races
baseball   basketball   other games
dodgeball   kickball

⑤ What sport would you like to play better?

football   handball   relay races
baseball   basketball   other games
dodgeball   kickball

⑥ Are you a good sport? (circle answer).

Yes   Sometimes   No

① Put a star ★ after your favorite subjects.

Math
Reading
Spelling
Science
Social Studies
P.E.
Art
Music
Writing stories and poems
Recess and lunch

② "I wish I could do better in ____."
(Underline answers).

Math
Spelling
Reading
P.E.
Science
Social Studies
Writing Stories and poems
Handwriting

③ Do you think this is going to be a good year for you?
(Underline your answer.)

Yes

No

Probably

Can't tell yet

Individualized Spelling Words

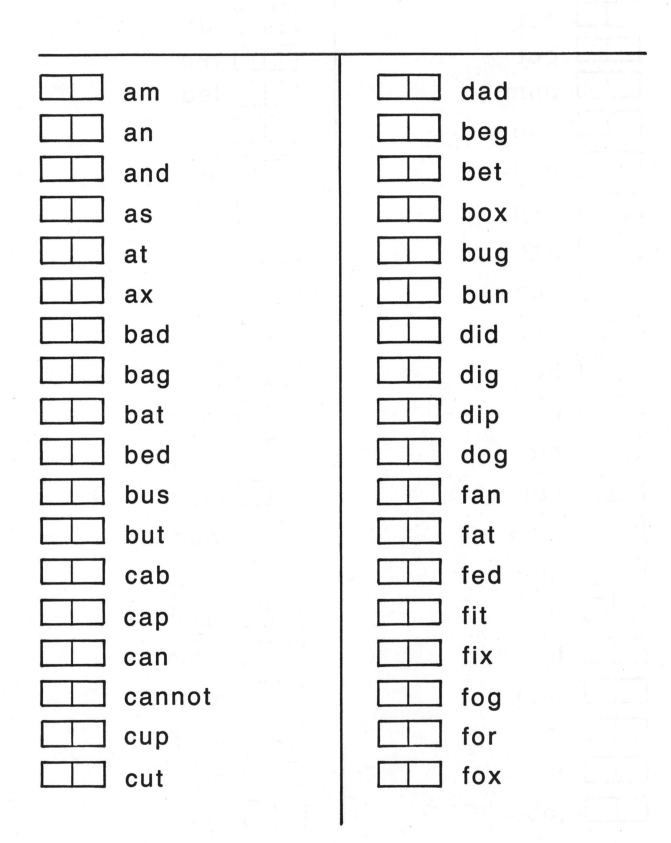

☐☐ am	☐☐ dad
☐☐ an	☐☐ beg
☐☐ and	☐☐ bet
☐☐ as	☐☐ box
☐☐ at	☐☐ bug
☐☐ ax	☐☐ bun
☐☐ bad	☐☐ did
☐☐ bag	☐☐ dig
☐☐ bat	☐☐ dip
☐☐ bed	☐☐ dog
☐☐ bus	☐☐ fan
☐☐ but	☐☐ fat
☐☐ cab	☐☐ fed
☐☐ cap	☐☐ fit
☐☐ can	☐☐ fix
☐☐ cannot	☐☐ fog
☐☐ cup	☐☐ for
☐☐ cut	☐☐ fox

☐☐ fun
☐☐ gas
☐☐ get
☐☐ got
☐☐ gum
☐☐ gun
☐☐ had
☐☐ ham
☐☐ hat
☐☐ hen
☐☐ hid
☐☐ him
☐☐ his
☐☐ hit
☐☐ hot
☐☐ hum
☐☐ hug
☐☐ if
☐☐ in
☐☐ into
☐☐ is
☐☐ it
☐☐ job

☐☐ jam
☐☐ jet
☐☐ kit
☐☐ lap
☐☐ led
☐☐ leg
☐☐ let
☐☐ lid
☐☐ lit
☐☐ lip
☐☐ log
☐☐ lot
☐☐ mad
☐☐ man
☐☐ map
☐☐ men
☐☐ met
☐☐ mix
☐☐ mom
☐☐ mop
☐☐ mud
☐☐ nap
☐☐ net

☐☐ not
☐☐ nut
☐☐ on
☐☐ pad
☐☐ pan
☐☐ pat
☐☐ pen
☐☐ pet
☐☐ pig
☐☐ pin
☐☐ pop
☐☐ pot
☐☐ pup
☐☐ rag
☐☐ ragbag
☐☐ ran
☐☐ rat
☐☐ red
☐☐ rid
☐☐ rip

☐☐ rob
☐☐ rub
☐☐ rag
☐☐ run
☐☐ sad
☐☐ sat
☐☐ set
☐☐ sit
☐☐ sip
☐☐ six
☐☐ sun
☐☐ tag
☐☐ tan
☐☐ tap
☐☐ ten
☐☐ tip
☐☐ top
☐☐ tub
☐☐ tug

Individualized Spelling Words

☐☐ and	☐☐ each
☐☐ as	☐☐ eat
☐☐ ask	☐☐ fast
☐☐ ate	☐☐ five
☐☐ best	☐☐ feel
☐☐ big	☐☐ fine
☐☐ boat	☐☐ go
☐☐ bath	☐☐ get
☐☐ bite	☐☐ give
☐☐ bake	☐☐ got
☐☐ cut	☐☐ game
☐☐ coat	☐☐ gift
☐☐ came	☐☐ glad
☐☐ did	☐☐ had
☐☐ day	☐☐ has
☐☐ drive	☐☐ help
☐☐ drop	☐☐ him
☐☐ drove	☐☐ hot

- [ ] his
- [ ] hole
- [ ] hand
- [ ] hunt
- [ ] held
- [ ] if
- [ ] into
- [ ] jump
- [ ] just
- [ ] keep
- [ ] kept
- [ ] let
- [ ] late
- [ ] made
- [ ] may
- [ ] make
- [ ] me
- [ ] much
- [ ] must
- [ ] mine
- [ ] milk
- [ ] no
- [ ] not
- [ ] name
- [ ] need
- [ ] nap
- [ ] note
- [ ] nut
- [ ] play
- [ ] pick
- [ ] plan
- [ ] red
- [ ] ran
- [ ] ride
- [ ] run
- [ ] reach
- [ ] read
- [ ] real
- [ ] rain
- [ ] road
- [ ] ride
- [ ] say
- [ ] see
- [ ] sing
- [ ] sit
- [ ] six

- so
- stop
- she
- seen
- seem
- stay
- swim
- stove
- sent
- stone
- save
- smoke
- same
- shape
- smile
- take
- tell
- ten

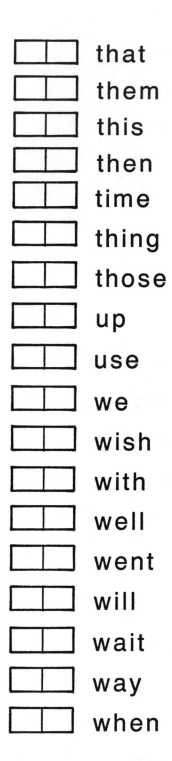

- that
- them
- this
- then
- time
- thing
- those
- up
- use
- we
- wish
- with
- well
- went
- will
- wait
- way
- when

Individualized Spelling Words

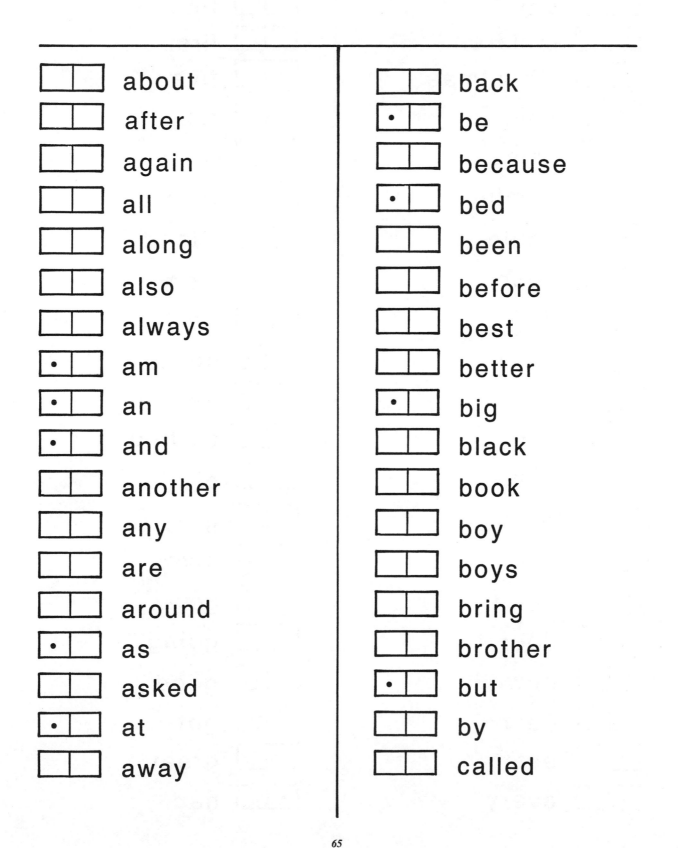

about	back
after	be
again	because
all	bed
along	been
also	before
always	best
am	better
an	big
and	black
another	book
any	boy
are	boys
around	bring
as	brother
asked	but
at	by
away	called

came
can
car
children
Christmas
cold
come
coming
could
country
day
days
dear
did
didn't
do
dog
don't
door
down
each
eat
every

father
few
find
first
five
for
found
four
friend
from
fun
gave
get
getting
girl
girls
give
go
going
good
got
great
had

happy
has
have
he
heard
help
her
here
him
his
home
hope
house
how
I
if
in
into
is
it
its
just
keep

kind
know
large
last
let
letter
like
little
live
long
look
looked
made
make
man
many
may
me
men
more
morning
most
mother

- much
- must
- my
- name
- never
- new
- next
- nice
- night
- no
- not
- now
- of
- off
- old
- on
- once
- one
- only
- or
- other
- our
- out

- over
- people
- place
- play
- please
- pretty
- put
- ran
- read
- red
- right
- room
- run
- said
- saw
- say
- school
- see
- she
- should
- small
- snow
- so

some
something
soon
started
summer
sure
• take
teacher
• tell
• than
• that
the
their
• them
• then
there
these
they
thing
things
think
• this
thought

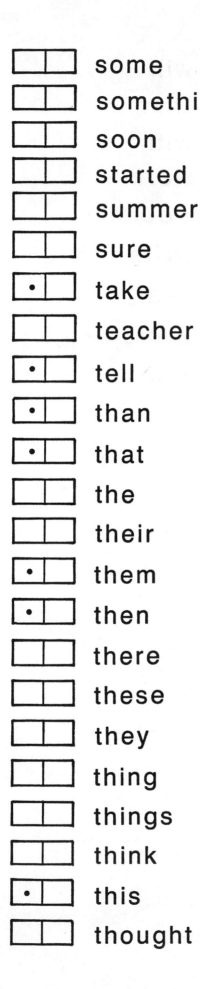

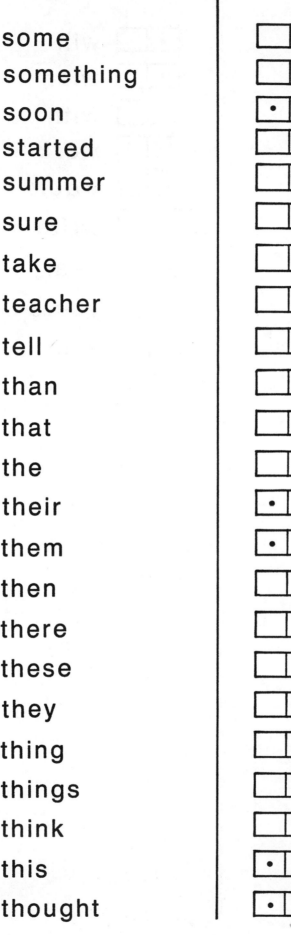

three
through
• time
to
today
told
too
took
town
tree
two
until
• up
• us
used
very
want
wanted
was
water
way
• we
• week

well
went
were
what
when
where
which
while
white
who

will
wish
with
work
would
write
year
years
you
your

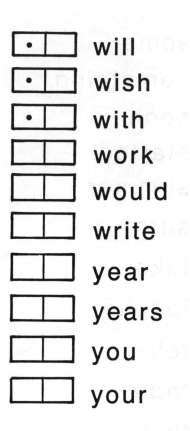

Individualized Spelling Words

- ☐☐ again
- ☐☐ all right
- ☐☐ always
- ☐☐ an
- ☐☐ and
- ☐☐ animals
- ☐☐ another
- ☐☐ around
- ☐☐ asked
- ☐☐ babies
- ☐☐ beautiful
- ☐☐ because
- ☐☐ before
- ☐☐ believe
- ☐☐ bought
- ☐☐ came
- ☐☐ caught
- ☐☐ children
- ☐☐ clothes
- ☐☐ coming
- ☐☐ course
- ☐☐ cousin
- ☐☐ decided
- ☐☐ didn't
- ☐☐ different
- ☐☐ dropped
- ☐☐ every
- ☐☐ February
- ☐☐ first
- ☐☐ for
- ☐☐ friend
- ☐☐ friends
- ☐☐ frightened
- ☐☐ from
- ☐☐ getting
- ☐☐ going

- happened
- hear
- heard
- here
- him
- interesting
- it's
- its
- jumped
- knew
- know
- let's
- like
- little
- looked
- many
- money
- morning
- mother
- name
- named
- off
- once
- our
- people
- pretty
- received
- running
- said
- school
- some
- something
- sometimes
- started
- stopped
- surprise
- swimming
- than
- that's
- their
- then
- there
- they
- they're
- things
- thought

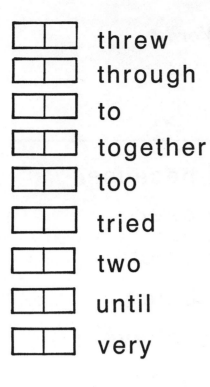

- threw
- through
- to
- together
- too
- tried
- two
- until
- very
- wanted
- went
- were
- when
- where
- with
- woman
- would
- you're

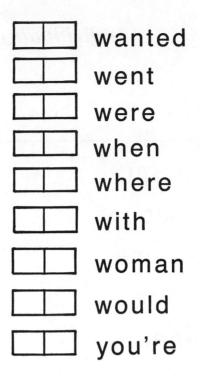

Individualized Spelling Words

- [ ] about
- [ ] account
- [ ] advise
- [ ] after
- [ ] again
- [ ] against
- [ ] ago
- [ ] almost
- [ ] also
- [ ] always
- [ ] American
- [ ] amount
- [ ] another
- [ ] any
- [ ] around
- [ ] asked
- [ ] attention
- [ ] away
- [ ] because
- [ ] been
- [ ] before
- [ ] being
- [ ] believe
- [ ] best
- [ ] better
- [ ] between
- [ ] business
- [ ] called
- [ ] cannot
- [ ] check
- [ ] city
- [ ] company
- [ ] copy
- [ ] could
- [ ] course
- [ ] credit

- ☐☐ days
- ☐☐ dear
- ☐☐ didn't
- ☐☐ does
- ☐☐ don't
- ☐☐ during
- ☐☐ enclosed
- ☐☐ enough
- ☐☐ even
- ☐☐ ever
- ☐☐ every
- ☐☐ eyes
- ☐☐ fact
- ☐☐ feel
- ☐☐ few
- ☐☐ find
- ☐☐ first
- ☐☐ found
- ☐☐ from
- ☐☐ general
- ☐☐ give
- ☐☐ given
- ☐☐ glad
- ☐☐ going
- ☐☐ good
- ☐☐ government
- ☐☐ great
- ☐☐ group
- ☐☐ have
- ☐☐ having
- ☐☐ head
- ☐☐ hear
- ☐☐ here
- ☐☐ herewith
- ☐☐ high
- ☐☐ himself
- ☐☐ house
- ☐☐ however
- ☐☐ information
- ☐☐ interest
- ☐☐ kind
- ☐☐ kindly
- ☐☐ knew
- ☐☐ know
- ☐☐ later
- ☐☐ letter

- [ ] little
- [ ] long
- [ ] love
- [ ] many
- [ ] matter
- [ ] might
- [ ] more
- [ ] morning
- [ ] most
- [ ] mother
- [ ] Mr.
- [ ] Mrs.
- [ ] never
- [ ] new
- [ ] next
- [ ] night
- [ ] note
- [ ] nothing
- [ ] number
- [ ] of
- [ ] office
- [ ] once
- [ ] one
- [ ] other
- [ ] our
- [ ] over
- [ ] own
- [ ] part
- [ ] people
- [ ] place
- [ ] please
- [ ] point
- [ ] possible
- [ ] present
- [ ] president
- [ ] price
- [ ] program
- [ ] public
- [ ] put
- [ ] receipt
- [ ] receive
- [ ] received
- [ ] return
- [ ] right
- [ ] room
- [ ] said

- school
- send
- sending
- sent
- service
- shall
- shipment
- should
- since
- sir
- small
- social
- some
- something
- soon
- state
- still
- sure
- system
- thank
- their
- there
- these
- they
- think
- those
- though
- thought
- three
- through
- to
- today
- told
- too
- toward
- try
- two
- under
- United States
- until
- upon
- use
- used
- very
- want
- war

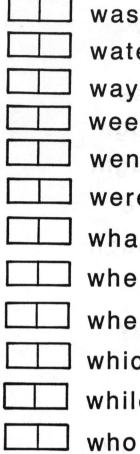

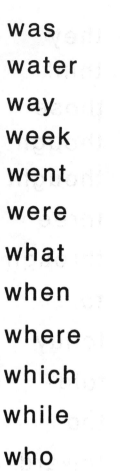

- was
- water
- way
- week
- went
- were
- what
- when
- where
- which
- while
- who
- why
- without
- work
- world
- would
- write
- year
- years
- young
- your
- yours

Individualized Spelling Words

☐☐ ache	☐☐ carrying
☐☐ again	☐☐ choose
☐☐ all right	☐☐ chose
☐☐ always	☐☐ color
☐☐ among	☐☐ coming
☐☐ answer	☐☐ cough
☐☐ any	☐☐ could
☐☐ been	☐☐ country
☐☐ before	☐☐ dear
☐☐ beginning	☐☐ doctor
☐☐ believe	☐☐ does
☐☐ blue	☐☐ done
☐☐ break	☐☐ don't
☐☐ built	☐☐ early
☐☐ business	☐☐ easy
☐☐ busy	☐☐ enough
☐☐ buy	☐☐ every
☐☐ can't	☐☐ February

☐☐ forty
☐☐ fourth
☐☐ friend
☐☐ grammar
☐☐ guess
☐☐ half
☐☐ having
☐☐ hear
☐☐ heard
☐☐ height
☐☐ here
☐☐ hoarse
☐☐ hole
☐☐ horse
☐☐ hour
☐☐ instead
☐☐ its
☐☐ it's
☐☐ just
☐☐ knew
☐☐ know
☐☐ laid
☐☐ loose

☐☐ lose
☐☐ making
☐☐ many
☐☐ meant
☐☐ minute
☐☐ much
☐☐ none
☐☐ often
☐☐ once
☐☐ passed
☐☐ past
☐☐ piece
☐☐ quiet
☐☐ quite
☐☐ raise
☐☐ read
☐☐ ready
☐☐ really
☐☐ receive
☐☐ said
☐☐ says
☐☐ seems
☐☐ separate

- [ ] shoes
- [ ] since
- [ ] some
- [ ] straight
- [ ] studying
- [ ] sugar
- [ ] sure
- [ ] tear
- [ ] than
- [ ] their
- [ ] then
- [ ] there
- [ ] they
- [ ] they're
- [ ] though
- [ ] through
- [ ] tired
- [ ] to
- [ ] tonight
- [ ] too
- [ ] tries
- [ ] trouble
- [ ] truly
- [ ] Tuesday
- [ ] two
- [ ] used
- [ ] using
- [ ] very
- [ ] wear
- [ ] Wednesday
- [ ] week
- [ ] where
- [ ] whether
- [ ] which
- [ ] whole
- [ ] whose
- [ ] women
- [ ] won't
- [ ] would
- [ ] write
- [ ] written
- [ ] writing
- [ ] wrote
- [ ] you're
- [ ] your

Individualized Spelling Words

er, ir, ur

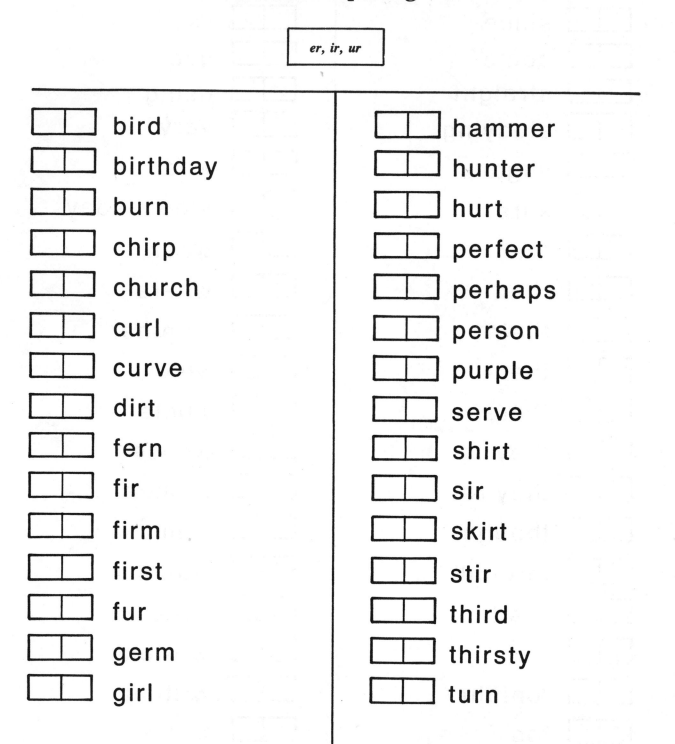

☐☐	bird	☐☐	hammer
☐☐	birthday	☐☐	hunter
☐☐	burn	☐☐	hurt
☐☐	chirp	☐☐	perfect
☐☐	church	☐☐	perhaps
☐☐	curl	☐☐	person
☐☐	curve	☐☐	purple
☐☐	dirt	☐☐	serve
☐☐	fern	☐☐	shirt
☐☐	fir	☐☐	sir
☐☐	firm	☐☐	skirt
☐☐	first	☐☐	stir
☐☐	fur	☐☐	third
☐☐	germ	☐☐	thirsty
☐☐	girl	☐☐	turn

Individualized Spelling Words

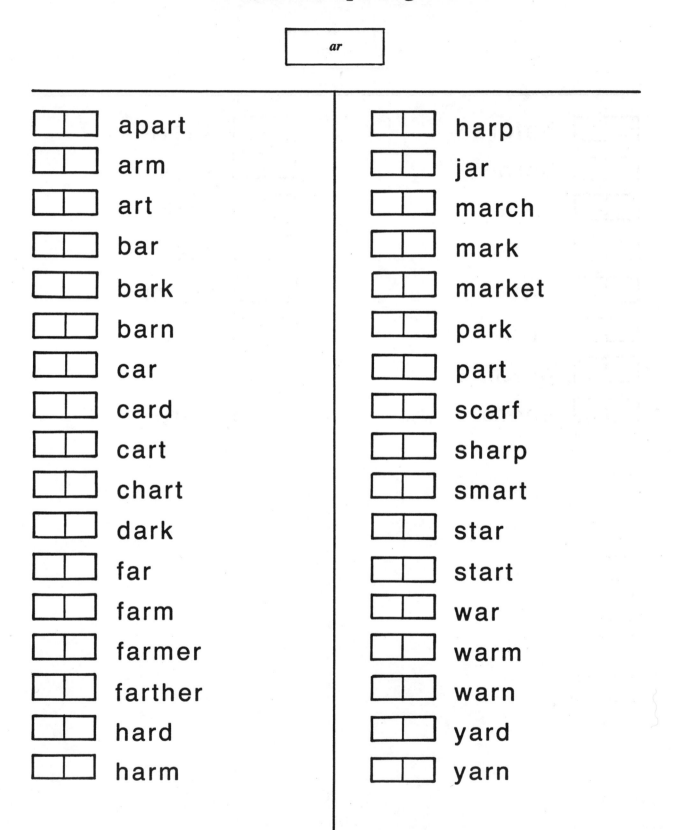

ar

- apart
- arm
- art
- bar
- bark
- barn
- car
- card
- cart
- chart
- dark
- far
- farm
- farmer
- farther
- hard
- harm
- harp
- jar
- march
- mark
- market
- park
- part
- scarf
- sharp
- smart
- star
- start
- war
- warm
- warn
- yard
- yarn

Individualized Spelling Words

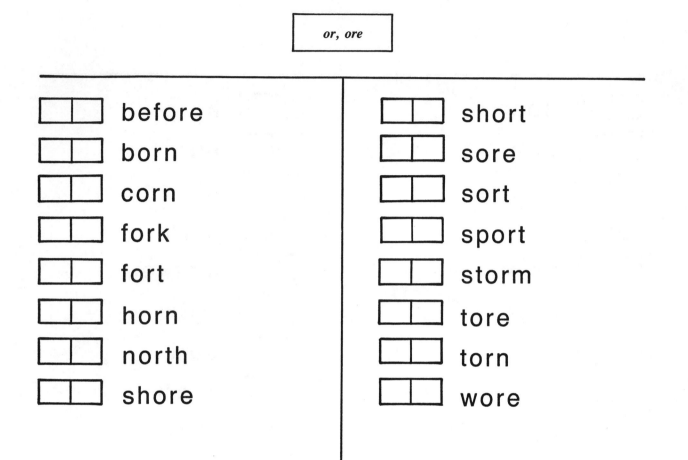

or, ore

☐☐ before	☐☐ short
☐☐ born	☐☐ sore
☐☐ corn	☐☐ sort
☐☐ fork	☐☐ sport
☐☐ fort	☐☐ storm
☐☐ horn	☐☐ tore
☐☐ north	☐☐ torn
☐☐ shore	☐☐ wore

Individualized Spelling Words

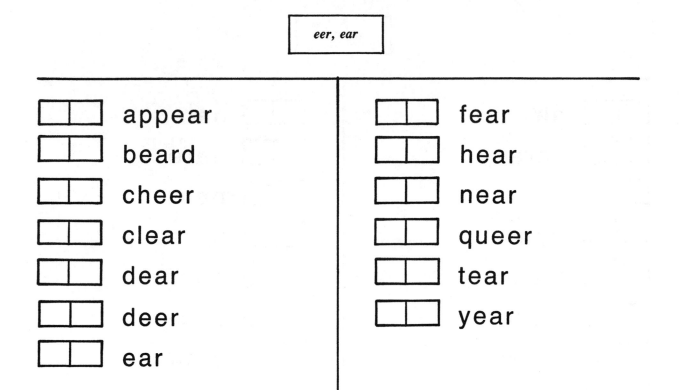

eer, ear

- appear
- beard
- cheer
- clear
- dear
- deer
- ear
- fear
- hear
- near
- queer
- tear
- year

Individualized Spelling Words

air, are

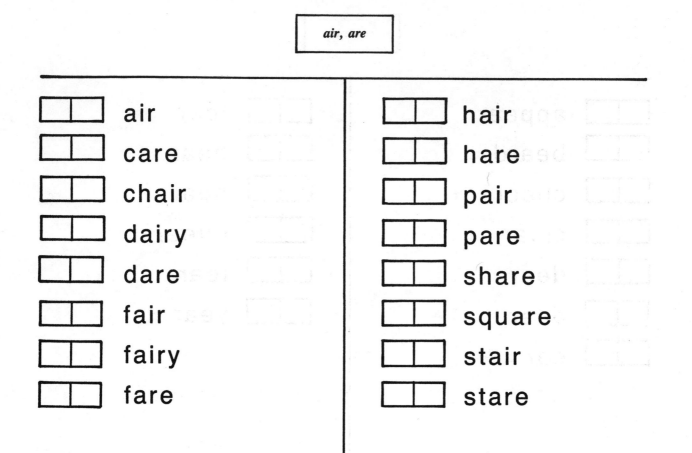

- air
- care
- chair
- dairy
- dare
- fair
- fairy
- fare
- hair
- hare
- pair
- pare
- share
- square
- stair
- stare

Individualized Spelling Words

au, aw

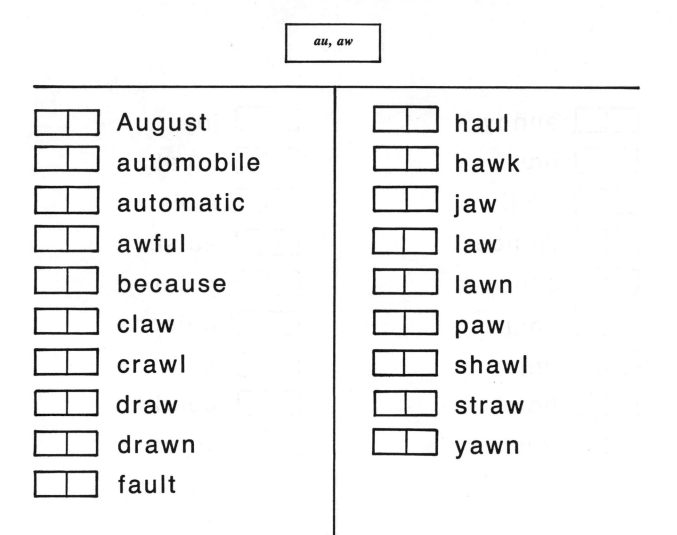

August	haul
automobile	hawk
automatic	jaw
awful	law
because	lawn
claw	paw
crawl	shawl
draw	straw
drawn	yawn
fault	

Individualized Spelling Words

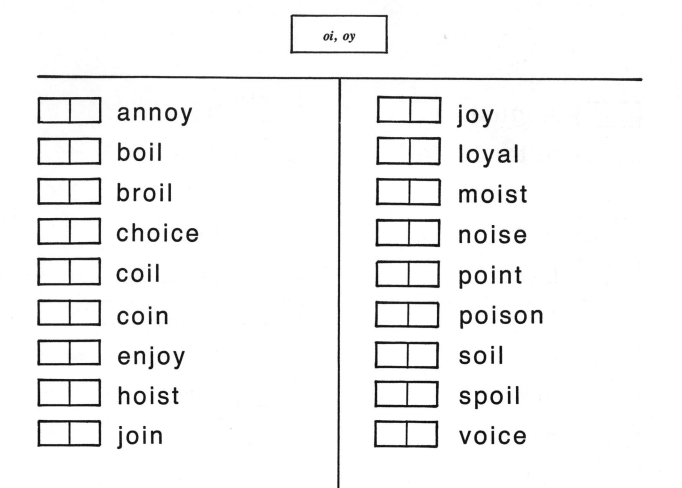

oi, oy

- annoy
- boil
- broil
- choice
- coil
- coin
- enjoy
- hoist
- join
- joy
- loyal
- moist
- noise
- point
- poison
- soil
- spoil
- voice

Individualized Spelling Words

ow, ō

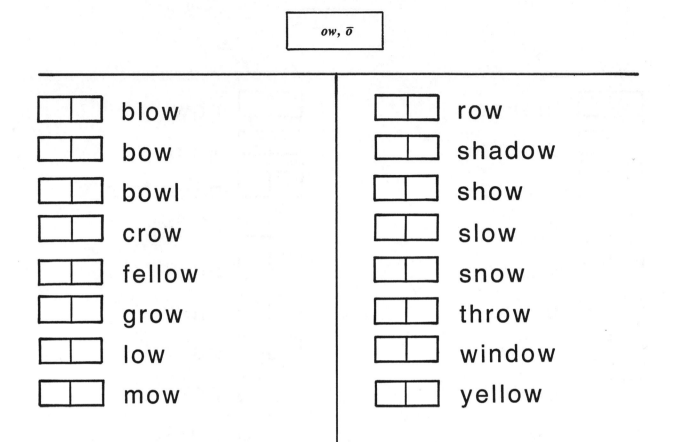

☐☐ blow	☐☐ row
☐☐ bow	☐☐ shadow
☐☐ bowl	☐☐ show
☐☐ crow	☐☐ slow
☐☐ fellow	☐☐ snow
☐☐ grow	☐☐ throw
☐☐ low	☐☐ window
☐☐ mow	☐☐ yellow

Individualized Spelling Words

ou, ow

- blouse
- bounce
- boundary
- bow
- brown
- cloud
- clown
- couch
- count
- crouch
- crowd
- crown
- drown
- flower
- found
- fountain
- ground
- growl
- hound
- howl
- loud
- mountain
- mouth
- our
- plow
- pound
- powder
- proud
- round
- scout
- scowl
- shout
- shower
- sound
- south
- towel
- tower
- town

Individualized Spelling Words

o͞o, ew

- [ ] blew
- [ ] bloom
- [ ] boom
- [ ] boot
- [ ] broom
- [ ] chew
- [ ] cool
- [ ] crew
- [ ] drew
- [ ] flew
- [ ] food
- [ ] grew
- [ ] igloo
- [ ] loop
- [ ] moon
- [ ] new
- [ ] noon
- [ ] room
- [ ] rooster
- [ ] scoop
- [ ] shoot
- [ ] smooth
- [ ] soon
- [ ] spool
- [ ] spoon
- [ ] stew
- [ ] stool
- [ ] threw
- [ ] tool
- [ ] tooth
- [ ] zoo

o͝o

- [ ] book
- [ ] foot
- [ ] look
- [ ] shook
- [ ] stood
- [ ] took
- [ ] wood
- [ ] wool

Individualized Spelling Words

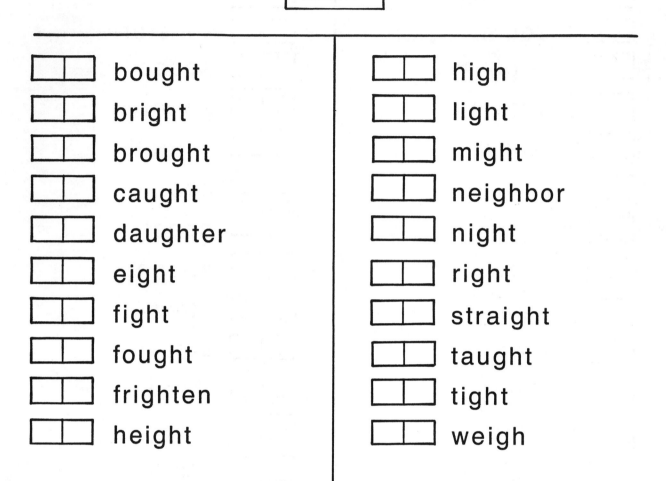

silent letters

☐☐ bought	☐☐ high
☐☐ bright	☐☐ light
☐☐ brought	☐☐ might
☐☐ caught	☐☐ neighbor
☐☐ daughter	☐☐ night
☐☐ eight	☐☐ right
☐☐ fight	☐☐ straight
☐☐ fought	☐☐ taught
☐☐ frighten	☐☐ tight
☐☐ height	☐☐ weigh

Individualized Spelling Words

silent letters

☐☐	knew	☐☐	wren
☐☐	knife	☐☐	write
☐☐	knock	☐☐	written
☐☐	know	☐☐	wrote
☐☐	known	☐☐	climb
☐☐	calf	☐☐	comb
☐☐	chalk	☐☐	crumb
☐☐	half	☐☐	lamb
☐☐	salmon	☐☐	limb
☐☐	stalk	☐☐	thumb
☐☐	talk	☐☐	castle
☐☐	walk	☐☐	fasten
☐☐	yolk	☐☐	listen
☐☐	whole	☐☐	often
☐☐	whose	☐☐	soften
☐☐	wrap	☐☐	whistle

Individualized Spelling Words

soft "c" and soft "g"

- ace
- advice
- age
- announce
- balance
- bounce
- cage
- ceiling
- celery
- cent
- center
- certain
- chance
- change
- citizen
- city
- dance
- danger
- December
- decide
- difference
- face
- fancy
- general
- gentle
- giant
- ginger
- huge
- ice
- juice
- lace
- large
- magic
- mice
- nice
- orange
- ounce
- package

Individualized Spelling Words

soft "c" and soft "g"

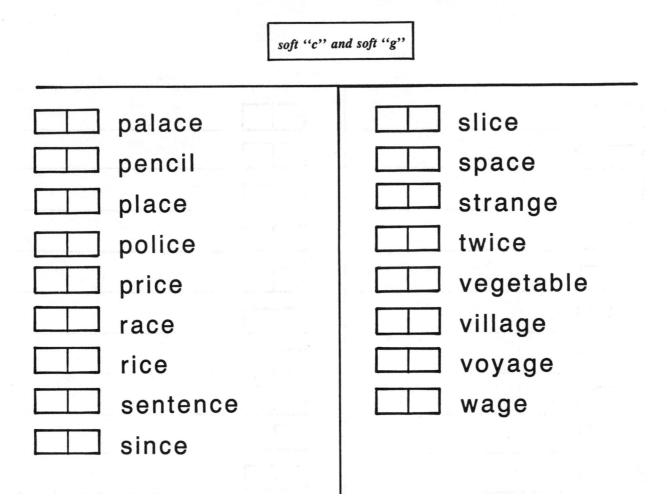

- palace
- pencil
- place
- police
- price
- race
- rice
- sentence
- since
- slice
- space
- strange
- twice
- vegetable
- village
- voyage
- wage

Words I Want to Learn